CORN-FED

poems by
JAMES STEVENSON
with illustrations by the author

GREENWILLOW BOOKS
An Imprint of HarperCollins*Publishers*

Printed in the United States of America.

First Avyx, Inc. Edition, 2010

ISBN 978-1-935570-00-4

Avyx, Inc.
8032 South Grant Way
Littleton, CO 80122
USA

Table of Contents

CORN-FED

poems by
JAMES STEVENSON
with illustrations by the author

GREENWILLOW BOOKS
An Imprint of HarperCollins*Publishers*

Corn-Fed: Poems
Copyright © 2002
by James Stevenson

All rights reserved.
Printed in Hong Kong by
South China Printing Co.
(1988) Ltd.
www.harperchildrens.com

Watercolor paints and a
black pen were used to
prepare the full-color art.

Library of Congress
Cataloging-in-Publication Data

Stevenson, James, (date)
Corn-fed / by James Stevenson.
    p.   cm.
"Greenwillow Books."
ISBN 0-06-000597-1 (trade).
ISBN 0-06-000598-X (lib. bdg.)
1. Children's poetry, American.
[1. American poetry.] I. Title.
PS3569.T4557 C65 2002
811'.54—dc21   2001033261

10 9 8 7 6 5 4 3 2 1
First Edition

For Chuck, with love

CONTENTS

Yesterday Larry sold
used cars.
Last night it snowed
and snowed.
Today he's selling hippos,
buffalo, and sheep.

I've been attacked by a rooster,

Kicked by a horse, chased by hornets,

And bitten by a seal.

Each time

I was surprised.

You never know

What's on somebody else's mind.

On my side of the table, it's ATO CHUP.

On your side, it's TOM KET.
But both are very good.

Want to take a picture

Of your chimney?

Want to get your cat

Out of a tree?

Want to get a little closer

To the moon?

Westside Rentals

Will be glad to help.

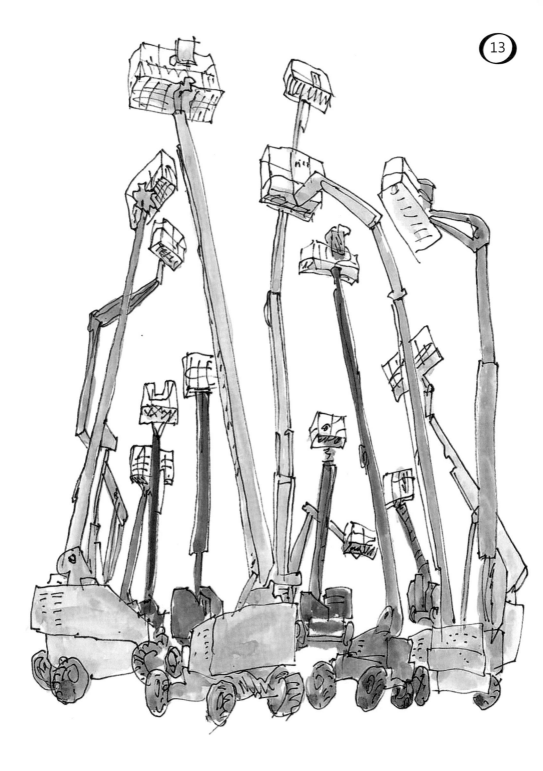

THE SIGN IN THE RESTAURANT WINDOW

MAKES YOU WONDER,

IS THIS A BOAST,

OR A WARNING?

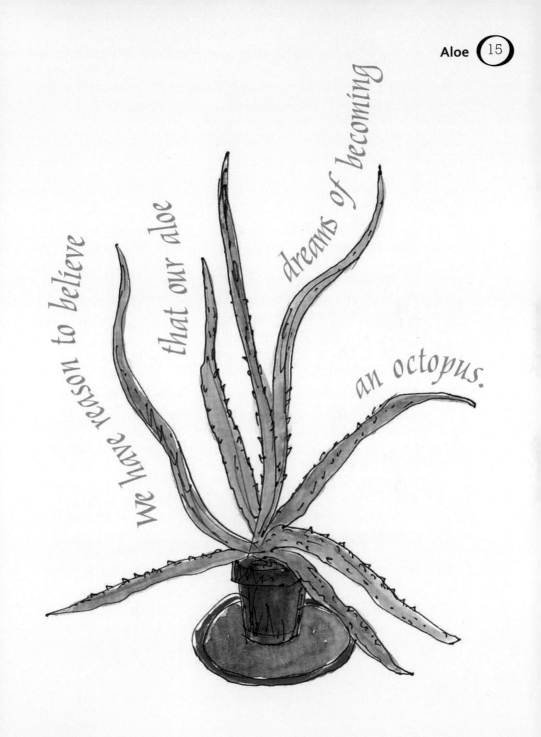

we have reason to believe that our aloe dreams of becoming an octopus.

Cold winds whip

Through their bones,

But summer will come,

And hot, noisy days

With many lives to guard.

If you take
3 tablespoons
of
mayonnaise,

1 cup
of
baking
powder,

3/4 cup
of
chunky
salsa,

1 pint
of
sour
cream,

1 teaspoon
of red
pepper,

2 teaspoons
of thyme,

3 tablespoons
of
mustard,

the juice of
4 lemons,

2 sweet pickles (chopped fine),

1 cup of olive oil,

4 tablespoons of creamy peanut butter,

2 cups of cocoa,

5 teaspoons of soy sauce,

2 cans of lentil soup, and mix together, put in a large pot, and let simmer for 2 hours, it still won't taste very good.

OVER THE YEARS

THE OLD GATE HAS DONE

A PRETTY GOOD JOB,

I GUESS. . . .

MOST OF THE ROCKS

ARE STILL THERE.

Somebody
brought
a red ball
to the park.

Some dogs stared at it.

Some
dogs
sniffed
it.

Some dogs dared it
to try and roll away

Some dogs
guarded it.

Some dogs chased it.

Some dogs
wrestled over it.

Some dogs
grabbed it and
chewed it.

And some dogs
just didn't care
at all.

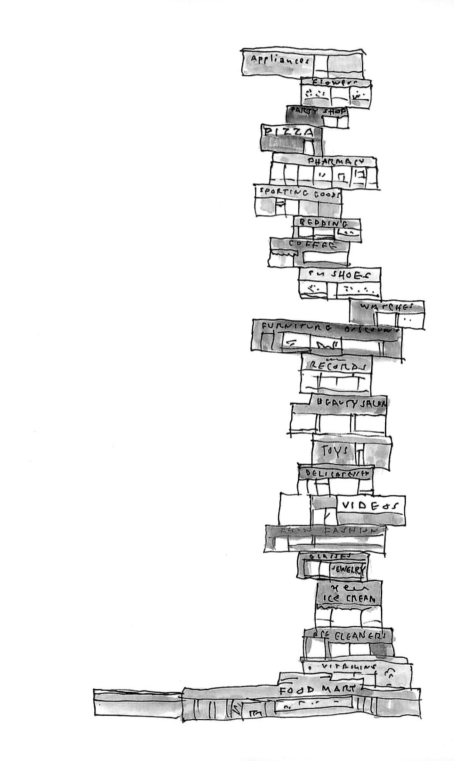

The Mall is
Such an ugly place.
Would it look better
If they

S
T
A
C
K
E
D
I
T
?

Not everything that runs

On the railroad tracks

Is a train.

But what these are,

You tell me.

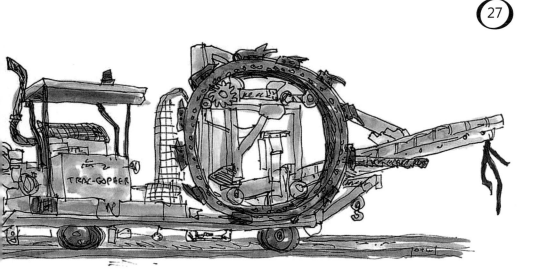

Compared to all

The skinny white yachts

In the marina,

This old tug is

One tough cookie.

The movie palace
Called the Shore
Closed years ago,
Says a man on the corner
With some time on his hands.
He says it was the best—
Double features all day long.
I'm wondering:
If you didn't like a movie,
Could you stand
On that fancy balcony and
Watch the Atlantic Ocean
Rolling in
And let some popcorn
Drift down seven stories
To the street?

Once a bike has discovered
What it's like
To run fast and free,
It just might try to escape.

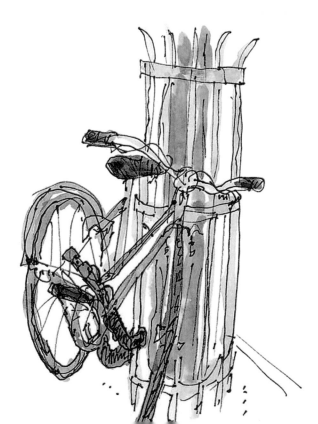

WHEN YOU WALK DOWN THE SIDEWALK,

MOST OF THE TIME YOU KNOW

WHAT THINGS ARE FOR,

BUT SOME OF THE TIME

YOU DON'T.

At the planetarium,
Small children stare
Out the windows
Of the buses,
Looking for the universe.

I love dawn,
Especially with
New York City
Under it.

When opossums get scared,

They pretend

To be dead.

But this one,

Lumbering across my path

At dawn,

Decided dying

Wouldn't work,

Since I had spotted him

In perfect health.

So he looked at me

With his two pink eyes,

And I looked at him

With my blues,

And we went

Our separate ways.

On the front of
The rusted mailbox,
You can make out
The words STORAGE BOX.
(But it doesn't say
For how long.)

Mt. Grunge

Mt. Everest

In the Himalayas

Is over 29,000 feet.

Mt. Grunge is only

A little over five,

But it is the highest peak

Of the Grimy Range,

Which runs along the side

Of Meadow Street,

At least until

The snow melts.

Want your shoes repaired?

Go to Mr. Girardi.

He's got everything he needs.

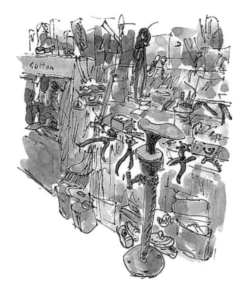

Mr. Girardi will get it done.

(He always does.)

Maybe not tomorrow,

But soon.

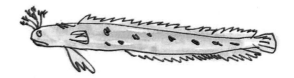

Did you ever wonder
Why fish look
So different,
While the rest of us
Look so much alike?

At the zoo,
Everybody looks at
The monkeys,
The birds,
The snakes,
The alligators,
The polar bears,
The penguins,

But nobody looks
    At the pigeons.

Cornflakes

Poems by
James Stevenson
with illustrations by the author

SCHOLASTIC INC.

New York Toronto London Auckland Sydney
Mexico City New Delhi Hong Kong

ISBN 0-439-29799-0

12 11 10 9 8 7 6 5 4 3 2 1   1 2 3 4 5 6/0

Printed in the U.S.A.   23

First Scholastic printing, April 2001

Watercolor paints and a black pen
were used for the full-color art.

For Jimmy

Contents

Somebody small and brave
  Left his Base Camp
At Pink Paper Plate,
Trekked across slippery Green Pickles,
Climbed over the Jagged Chips,
Grabbed an Onion Curl
And swung across to Lower Bun.
He slogged through
Mayo, Mustard, Melted Cheese,

Then crept up Burger Cliff
And on to Upper Bun,
And on the summit proudly stuck
The small blue flag of Cellophane.

In the park
The fathers
Teach the kids
Everything
They'll need to know:

How to catch,

How to throw,

How to hit,

And how to tie their shoes.

Banged-up tables,

Busted sofas,

Chairs with broken arms

 and legs

Wait for Mr. Belfont

(Doctor of furniture)

To make them

Good as new.

I'd like to make

One painting

Half as nice

As my paint box

Left alone.

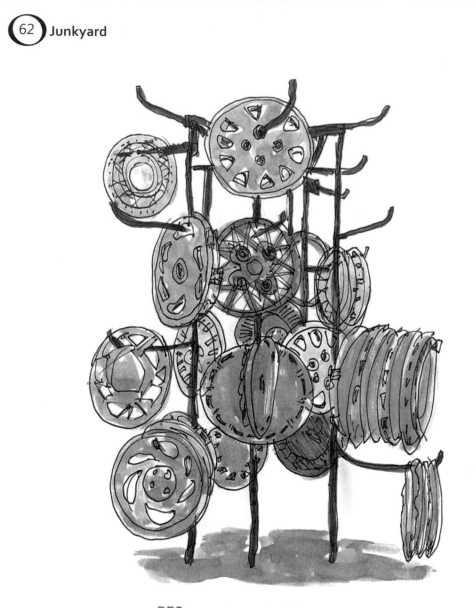

When the wind blows
Through the junkyard
You can hear the hubcaps
C l a n g .

One day
Our paperwhite narcissus
Declared,
"I am too lovely
And I smell too sweet,"

And swooned.

Packed in ice,

The *Island Queen*

Waits out the winter,

Waiting for July—

For flags,

Warm winds,

And ice cream.

Loyal and true,
My wastebasket
Says yes to everything.
"NOT BAD! . . . QUITE GOOD! . . .
OH, EXCELLENT! . . .
ARE YOU SURE
YOU DON'T WANT THAT BACK?"

Hard workers,
one and all,
They ratt-
le down
the road together,
Heading for the job.

"May I borrow

A cup of sugar?"

Calls Number 139.

"Certainly," says 141.

"I'll meet you downstairs."

THERE'S A FACTORY
ON THE POST ROAD.
YOU CAN'T TELL
WHAT IT MAKES.
MAYBE IT
DOESN'T MAKE
ANYTHING.
MAYBE IT JUST
BREATHES IN AND OUT.

Every day
The bent old woman
Shuffles down the sidewalk,
Inch by inch.

From in front,
She has no face.

From behind,
She has no head.

All you see is
Her coat, her cane, her courage.

*O*utside, cold branches
Scrape the glass.
Inside, the jungle
Blooms.

I CAN'T MOVE MOUNTAINS.

I CAN'T STOP THE CLOCK.

I CAN'T CURE THE COMMON COLD.

BUT I CAN MAKE IT SNOW IN CHICAGO.

If you go past the

Outdoor furniture shop,

You'll see there is

More than one way

To take a load off.

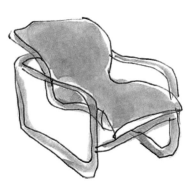

It's Garbage Day in the City.

The Bags Sit on the Sidewalk,

Dressed in Black,

Wearing Bow Ties,

READY FOR THE OPERA.

Every day the basket man puts all his baskets out.

Every night the basket man puts all his baskets in.

Along the shore

The perfect shell

Awaits the perfect child.

The Fenders, the Martins,

The Gretsches, the Gibsons

Hang from their hooks

On the music store ceiling,

Waiting for someone

To set their sound free.

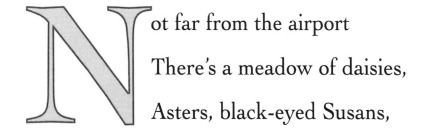

ot far from the airport

There's a meadow of daisies,

Asters, black-eyed Susans,

Buicks, Pontiacs, and Queen Anne's lace.

At the concrete plant
It's feeding time:
The fat white trucks
Crowd in,
Piglets
with
upturned
snouts.

IF YOU ALWAYS WALK
➡ STRAIGHT AHEAD
YOU'LL PROBABLY MISS
WHAT'S JUST
AROUND THE
CORNER

All along the island road,

everybody's got a ride,

one way or another.

TAKE-OUT MENU

APPETIZERS / SIDE DISHES

SANDWICHES AND LIGHT MEALS

LINGUINI DISHES

ENTREES

SEAFOOD

"Clam Cakes," he said.
"I'll have Clam Cakes."
                    "No . . .
Fried Shrimp . . . Wait . . .
Lobster Salad . . . No . . .
Filet of Fish . . . Hold it.
Fried Calamari!"

"Veggie Stir-Fry . . . No . . .
Wait . . .
Salad Bowl . . . !"

I t was a foggy day on the island—
Bad luck for visitors who came to see

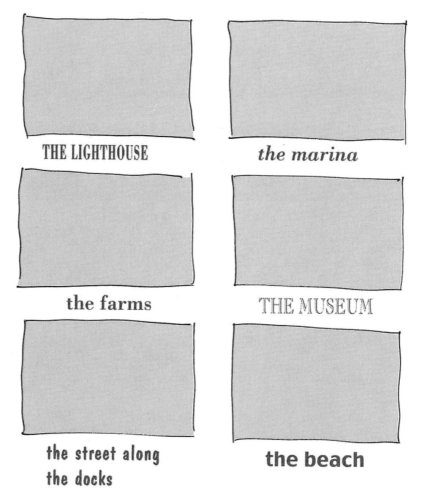

THE LIGHTHOUSE

the marina

the farms

THE MUSEUM

the street along
the docks

the beach

Until . . .
The sun burned through,
And it was a perfect day for visitors.

Corn Chowder

Poems by
James Stevenson
with illustrations by the author

Greenwillow Books
An Imprint of HarperCollins Publishers

Corn Chowder
Copyright © 2003
by James Stevenson
All rights reserved.
Manufactured in China.
www.harperchildrens.com

Watercolor paints and a black
pen were used to prepare
the full-color art.

Library of Congress
Cataloging-in-Publication Data

Stevenson, James, (date).
Corn chowder /
by James Stevenson.
    p.   cm.
"Greenwillow Books."
Summary: A collection of
short poems with titles such
as "At the National Zoo,"
"Cell Phone," and
"Backpack Mystery."
ISBN 0-06-053059-6 (trade).
ISBN 0-06-053060-X (lib. bdg.)
1. Children's poetry, American.
[1. American poetry.]   I. Title.
PS3569.T4557 C64 2003
811'.54—dc21   2002009111

1 2 3 4 5 6 7 8 9 10
First Edition

For Leo, with love

Contents

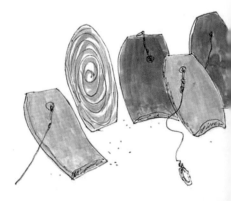

In the city, dogs are put in charge of . . .

trees,

signs,

and parking meters.

At Harry's Fresh Flowers,

everything is bright and cheerful.

Except Harry.

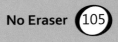

Plenty of pencil left, but the eraser's gone.
Somebody must keep changing his mind.

The baby elephant runs.

It stands in a tub and a tire

It walks under
its mother.

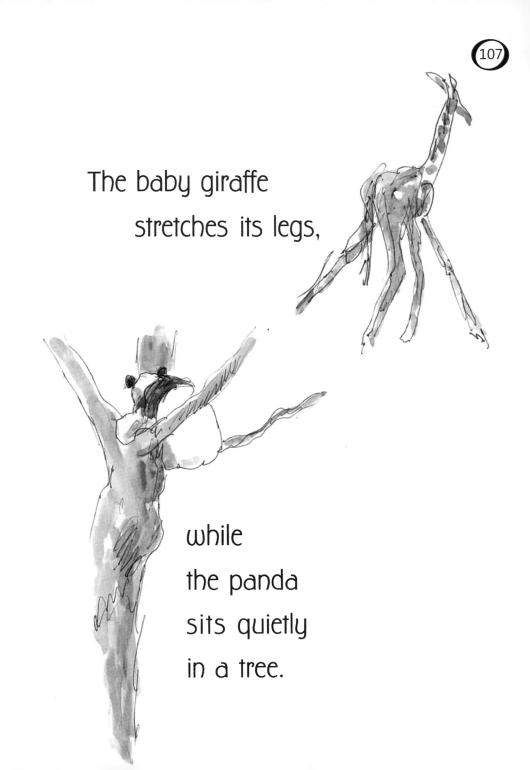

The baby giraffe
stretches its legs,

while
the panda
sits quietly
in a tree.

When you think
everything is
falling apart,
look how many ways
there are
to hold things
together.

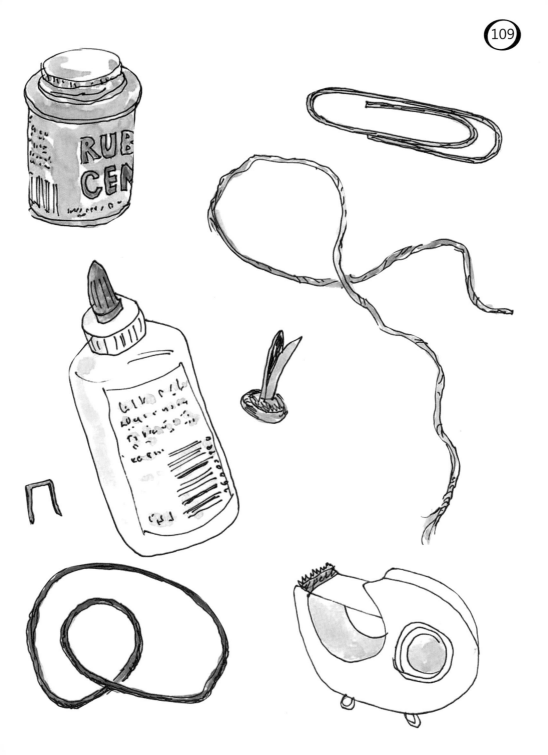

Some climb up.

Some slide down.

Some fly in the air.

Some sit . . .

and watch.

Some whirl around.

Some **bounce.**

Some eat SNACKS.

Some sleep in the shade.

Some take one more slide.

And some go home.

TO PEOPLE I HEAR TALKING
LOUDLY ON THEIR CELL PHONES

It is **VERY IMPORTANT**
to take care of your cell phone!
Do you know how?

The best way is to drop it in
a deep pot of chicken fat
and bring to a boil.

Simmer for two hours.

Let cool.

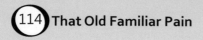

OW! OW! OW!
It feels like somebody shot an arrow
through my forehead . . .
OW!

But wait . . . The pain is
slowly going away . . . Ahhhh . . .
It's gone, and now it's safe
(I hope) to take another bite
of that icy-cold,
delicious
ice cream.

Did you ever have an idea come along,

a pretty good idea,

and the more you thought about it,

the better it got

and the fancier it got

until it was
a really great idea,

one of
the best ideas
you ever had,

but then somebody else said, **"What a dumb idea!"**

and it all fell down . . .

and you had to wait for the next idea?

I wish I had lived one hundred years ago in Mexico.
I would have been a VAQUERO, rounding up cattle,

WEARING A HAT LIKE THIS.

Or I would have been a cowboy in Texas, with a saddle like this . . .

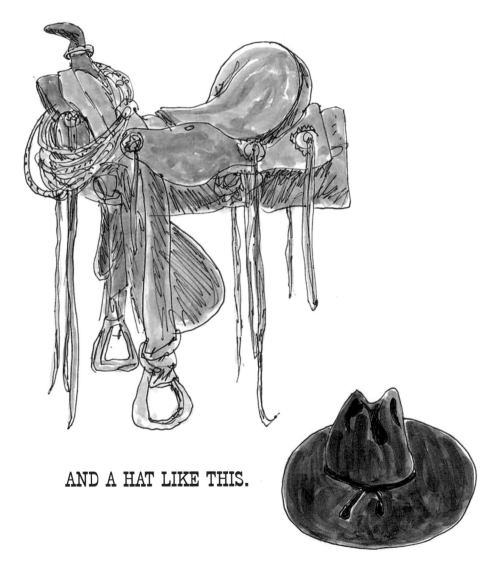

AND A HAT LIKE THIS.

When I go to the drugstore and

I am grateful to be

see how many ailments there are,

ALIVE.

Everybody's
waiting
for something
in the city:

for the talk to end,

for a taxi,

for the bus to arrive,

for the time to pass,

for the light to change,

for the truck to come.

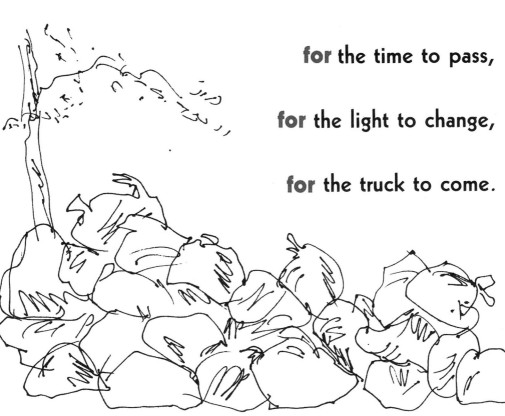

The children go to school with backpacks so big, it makes you wonder what's inside them.

A BOWLING BALL?

A CINDER BLOCK?

A BOX OF JELLY DOUGHNUTS?

AN ACCORDION?

A PUMPKIN?

THE FAMILY DOG?

A BOWL OF GOLDFISH

BREAD, BOLOGNA, MUSTARD?

CHEESE, LETTUCE, MAYO?

200 TRADING CARDS?

A DOZEN OVERDUE LIBRARY BOOKS?

TWO SKATEBOARDS?

A RAINCOAT, A TENT, AND A SLEEPING BAG?

MORE HAIR RIBBONS AND AN ELECTRIC IRON?

A WEEK'S SUPPLY OF JELLY BEANS?

EVERYTHING YOU COULD NEED IN THE COURSE OF THE YEAR?

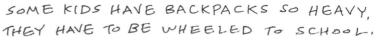

SOME KIDS HAVE BACKPACKS SO HEAVY, THEY HAVE TO BE WHEELED TO SCHOOL.

*An American Goldfinch
is at work on his "Field Guide to Human Beings."*

A can of paint

always

has more in it

than you need,

and it

lives with you

for the rest of your life.

The museum is a good place

for the very young . . .

and the very old . . .

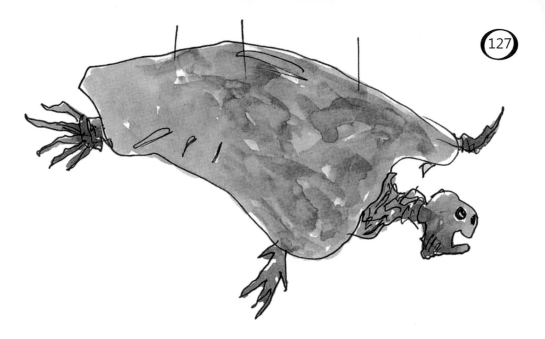

and the *very* brave.

Do you ever wonder how much peanut butter you have had in your life?

I have had
THIS *much,*
and I am about to buy another jar.

Under the bridge where the highway crosses the river,

somebody has put a folding chair.

Maybe the person just likes to eat his lunch

and listen to the thunder of the traffic overhead.

Q: *What do you get when you take small children to breakfast at the diner?*

IF you look
in the locksmith's window,
you'll see there is more
than one way to open a door.

Trees on the sidewalks grow

in boxes of dirt,

in bricks,

behind bars,

inside wire fences,

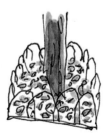

in gravel.

The trees don't always make it,

but a lot of the time they do.

On a sweltering night in July in the city,
the snack wagon rolled out of its garage.
It rattled down the empty streets
and into Central Park.

When a breeze came up,

    the snack wagon went for a sail on the lake.

    Then it rolled back home to the garage,

    leaving only a trail of drips.

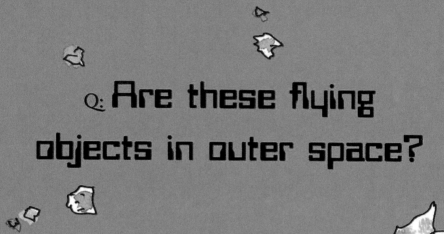

Q: Are these flying objects in outer space?

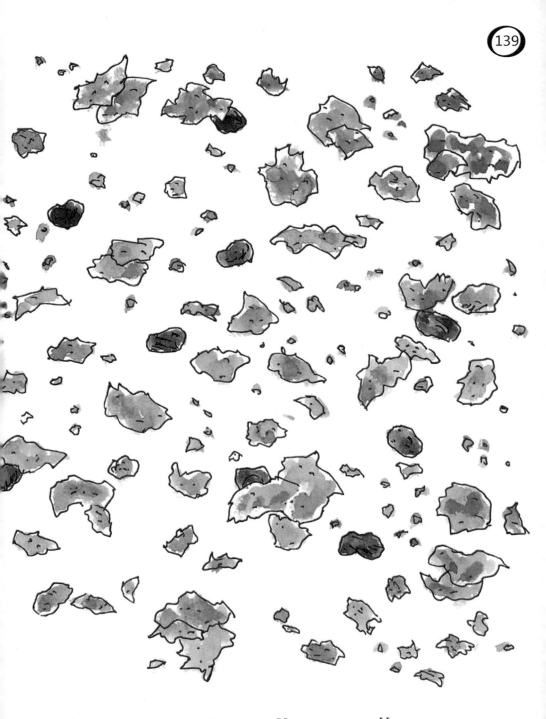

A: No. This is what happened when I dropped the box of Raisin Bran on the kitchen floor.

Sometimes I wish the turnpike was

the way it used to be.

There's a noise so loud,

there is
nothing
louder . . .

than Uncle Carl eating his sweet corn chowder.

SWEET
CORN

POEMS
BY JAMES
STEVENSON

WITH ILLUSTRATIONS
BY THE AUTHOR

A BEECH TREE
PAPERBACK BOOK
NEW YORK

Watercolor paints and a black pen
were used for the full-color art.

Copyright © 1995 by
James Stevenson

The Library of Congress has
cataloged the Greenwillow Books
edition of <u>Sweet Corn</u> as follows:
Stevenson, James (date)
Sweet corn / by James Stevenson.
p. cm.
Summary: A collection of short
poems with titles such as "Screen
Door," "Bike Rental," and "Photo
Album."
ISBN 0-688-12647-2
1. Children's poetry, American.
[1. American poetry.] I. Title.
PS3569.T4557S94
1995 811'.54—dc20
94-4902 CIP AC

10 9 8 7 6 5 4 3 2
First Beech Tree Edition, 1999
ISBN 0-688-17304-7

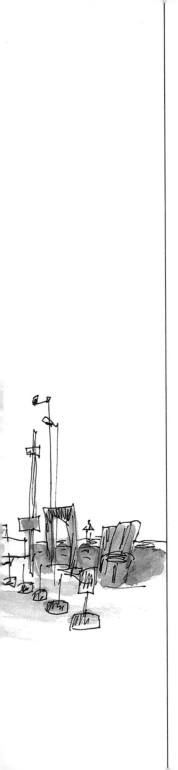

FOR AVA

Contents

WHY AM I HAPPY THAT I WAS BORN?

JUST ONE REASON (IN SEASON):

There's a tree house
    Up in the apple tree,
A platform of planks
Jammed between the branches.
To get there,
Climb a stairway of sticks
Nailed to the trunk
Like a busted xylophone.
Mountaineers and pirates
Ascend and descend,
Busy as inchworms.

How many are up there now?
It's anybody's guess:
Green leaves keep it secret.
Could be no one, could be three.
Could be ten
With peanut butter
sandwiches
And an excellent
view of France.

If you started with sap green,
Added raw umber,
Maybe some violet,
You might get the sky.

For the sea you'd need cobalt,
Alizarin Crimson,
Possibly ochre,
Ultramarine.

But the faraway ferryboat
Slicing between them,
White as a snowflake
Against a black tree trunk,

They can't make that color.
So leave it plain paper.
Then darken the sky
And darken the sea.

Cows mostly
Seldom climb
Don't travel
Like to

stand there,

mountains,

widely,

stay home.

At the side of the road a man sells old windows,

Hundreds of windows, losing their paint.

They lean every which way,

Stacked against tree trunks.

The man looks as old as the windows he sells.

At times you don't see him . . . he's lost in the sunlight,

Waist-high in diamonds, half-sunk in ice.

He'll sell you a window.

Then when you look through it,

Decide for yourself which is indoors or out.

BIG KIDS
ALWAYS SIT IN
LITTLE KID

BIG
KIDS
SEE WHAT'
LITTLE KIDS NEVER SE

HE FRONT SEAT

ET STUCK IN THE BACK

COMING

NYTHING TILL IT'S OVER

Early in the rainy morning
My fat black dog
Rolls off the sofa,
Ambles to the doorway and,
Using her flat forehead
   as a battering ram,
Hits the bottom left corner
   of the screen door,
Sends it flying open—crash!

She walks out onto the porch,
Toenails clicking on the boards.
The screen door slams
    behind her,
A cannon announcing dawn.
Picking a good observation post,
She settles down
    on the wet wood
And takes command of the day.

If there's something you want,

This store doesn't have it.

Well, maybe they have it,

But somebody put it

Over or under some place

Where they lost it.

They say they could get it

(But not very soon).

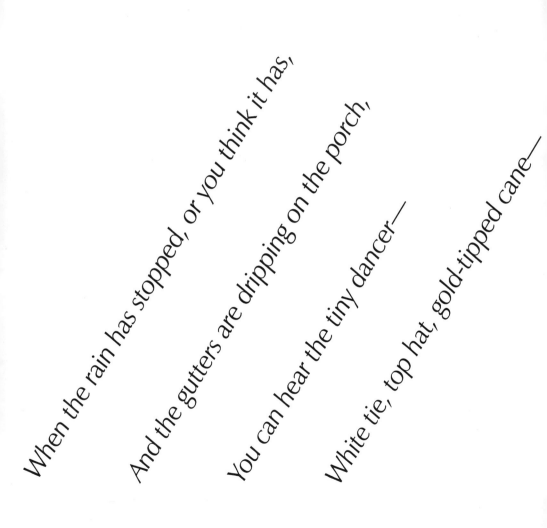

When the rain has stopped, or you think it has,

And the gutters are dripping on the porch,

You can hear the tiny dancer—

White tie, top hat, gold-tipped cane—

Spattering his taps around the boards:

Time-step toe-drop shuffle brush hop.

Then the sun—

scuff scoot—

Comes out.

Young and old people
Lean over the railings,
Clutching thin strings
That go down to the water.

Maybe they're fishing.
Maybe they're crabbing.
Maybe they're flying their kites
Upside down.

VACANCY / NO VACANCY

POSTCARDS / SOUVENIRS

SALTWATER TAFFY

INDIAN JEWELRY

WATER SLIDE

REPTILE FARM

BANDIT'S CAVE

NATIVE HONEY

RIVER RAFTING

MINI-GOLF

LOOKOUT MOUNTAIN

BAR-B-Q

FALLING ROCKS

WAX MUSEUM

BASEBALL CARDS

VACANCY/NO VACANCY

WHEN THE GOO

THE THICK DOOR AT

WHITE TRUCK, DRY

INTO THE SUNLIGH

FRIGID AIR SWOO

THAT WAS LOADE

HUMOR MAN OPENED

HE BACK OF HIS

CE CLOUDS BILLOWED

VE COULD FEEL THE

ROM THE DIM CAVERN

WITH ICE CREAM.

The ladder leaning against the barn

Is like the man who used to use it:

Strong at the beginning,

Okay in the middle,

A few rungs missing at the end.

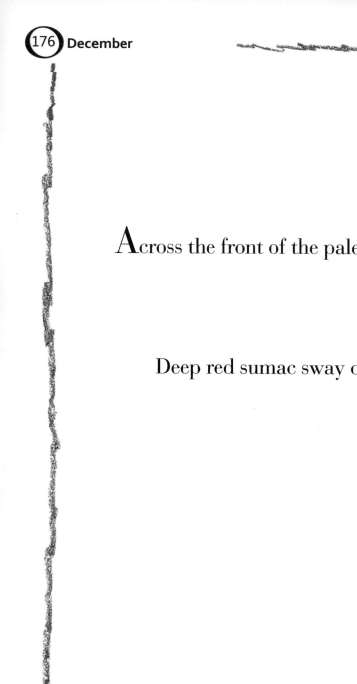

Across the front of the pale gray woods

Deep red sumac sway on stilts.

Clusters of half-notes

Scribble a crimson score.

When fog blurs the morning,
  Porches glisten, shingles drip.
  Droplets gather on the green screen door.
"Look," they say to one another,
"Look how dry it is inside."

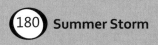

WHEN THE THUNDERSTORM COMES

PUNCHING ITS WAY THROUGH TOWN,

THE DOG STICKS HER NOSE UNDER THE SOFA.

ALL OF US FLINCH AS THE LIGHTNING HITS,

REVEALED AS CRINGING COWARDS IN THE FLASH.

RAIN HURLS ITSELF INTO THE STREET.

THE OLD HOUSE TREMBLES.

BUT EVERYBODY KNOWS

WHEN THIS LETS UP AND THE SKY TURNS BLUE,

WE'LL THROW OUR SNEAKERS OFF AND RACE

TO MUDDY PUDDLES DEEP AND WARM

AND KICK THE WATER BACK INTO THE SKY.

I won't say what I said.

You won't say what you said.

They won't say what they said.

Nobody will cry.

That's the way it will be.

Next time.

Walking the dog on a freezing beach,
I saw two—what? You couldn't call them ships.
Barges? Dredges? Ungainly, eccentric.
The small one a dragon, a dinosaur maybe:
Drill for a nose, hose for a tail,
Two rusty horns sticking into the sky.

The big barge—or dredge—was more like a castle,
A watchtower watching the kingdom of rust.
Bundled-up yeomen preparing odd weapons,
Thinking the dragon might slowly attack?

But what kind of battle could happen between them?
Spitting some mud, and then drifting home?

If I were a king, I'd want this kind of castle.
And next to my castle, a dragon like that.

Free from bedrooms, bathrooms, kitchen,

Flapping, snapping in the breeze,

Only a handful of clothespins

Keeps them from flying

to Spain.

On mornings in August

His store is a table.

To joggers and bikers

He sells lemonade.

But when the sun blazes

And nobody's buying,

He makes an umbrella

Out of his store.

Look at the pictures: Everyone's smiling.
Old friends are posing, giggling and hugging.
Birthdays and weddings, mountains and beaches,
Brothers and sisters, grandmas and babies.
Nobody's angry, nobody's crying,
Nobody's fighting, nobody dies.

Somewhere in the darkrooms
Where pictures get developed,
Sloshed around in chemicals
Beneath a dim red light
Those other pictures vanished,
Somewhere in the darkness,
Somehow disappeared there,
Never did come out.

Look at the pictures: Everyone's smiling.
Old friends are posing, giggling and hugging.
Birthdays and weddings, mountains and beaches,
Brothers and sisters, grandmas and babies.
Nobody's angry, nobody's crying,
Nobody's fighting, nobody dies.